SAVING CRANBERRY

A true story about how my mommy
rescued a baby alligator turtle.

Domarina E. Pace

www.savingcranberry.com

ISBN: 978-0-692-54199-9

Published by Domarina E. Pace,
www.savingcranberry.com

Printed in the U.S.A.
Signature Book Printing, www.sbpbooks.com

for Jacob

I love the Thanksgiving holiday. Each year, my Mommy makes the most delicious cranberry sauce, and I get to help her in the kitchen.

We begin by washing the fresh cranberries, in a big bowl filled with water.

As the crimson red colored berries float and bounce to our fingertips back and forth, I imagine jumping in a pool filled with bouncy balls. What a wonderful feeling.

Then, Mommy pours the cranberries in a big pot on the stove top, adds water and sugar, and starts to stir up.

She stirs and stirs, with lots of love, until the sweet smell of the sauce fills our house.

Now, the cranberry sauce is ready.

At last, she pours the cranberry sauce in small jars and seals them, until Thanksgiving arrives.

We always share our cranberry sauce with family, friends and neighbors.

I enjoy taking the cranberry sauce to our neighbors because I get to say hello and wish them a happy Thanksgiving.

One autumn day before Thanksgiving, while Mommy was preparing to make her delicious sauce, something very strange happened in our kitchen!

Just as she opened a bag of fresh cranberries, poured them in the bowl, and was about to wash them, she noticed something much bigger than a cranberry.

"Maybe a wood chip," she thought!

Mommy looked closer and was startled! Indeed, it was not a wood chip.

"Oh no, it looks like a baby turtle!" she exclaimed.

"But what is a baby turtle doing in a bag of fresh cranberries?"
With wonderment, she thought about where cranberries grow! *"In swamps and rivers, or a sandy bog, and what if the baby turtle got lost?"*

Mommy was concerned. The baby turtle was not moving.
She had an idea, *"How about scooping the baby turtle out of the cranberry bowl?"*
So, she carefully did.

Still, the baby turtle was not moving.

Anxiously, she called my Daddy. *"Honey, you won't believe what came out of a bag of fresh cranberries..."*

Suddenly, she started to scream, *"He's moving! He's alive! Let me pour some water in the jar! I'll call you back honey..."*

Sure enough, as soon as the water hit the baby turtle, he opened his eyes, and cautiously stretched his tail.

"Oh my, what a long tail he has," she thought.

Mommy was very joyous and thankful to see the baby turtle alive, so she named him Cranberry.

Meanwhile, Cranberry needed special care, so she called the animal shelter.

After listening to Mommy's story, Joan at the shelter said to bring the baby turtle in.

Mommy drove Cranberry to the animal shelter.
"Maybe he could come back and live with us!" She thought.

At the shelter, the veterinarian examined Cranberry and his long tail and broke the news to Mommy...

She said, *"He is a baby alligator turtle and not native to California. Instead, his long journey started far, far away, among the wildlife of swamps and rivers in Texas."*

Somehow, Cranberry had to return home.

At the shelter, Officer J.R. volunteered to foster the baby alligator turtle until he was big and strong enough to travel back home to Texas.

Officer J.R. made a temporary home out of a fish tank for Cranberry and started to care for him.

Sadly, Cranberry could not live with us in California, but it was truly a miracle to be rescued in our kitchen.

Mommy tearfully said goodbye to baby alligator turtle, but she knew he was in good hands.

She thought for a moment: *"It is Cranberry's destiny to go back home someday where he could freely swim in rivers and swamps, play with other alligator turtles, and live happily ever after."*

~ The End ~

Thank you officer Joseph Robert Stewart
for fostering and sending me back home.

-Cranberry